HANCOCK'S BREWERY

WIVELISCOMBE

MARY MILES

GW00777098

Published by

THE SOMERSET INDUSTRIAL

ARCHAEOLOGICAL SOCIETY

1985

CONTENTS

ACKNOWLEDGEMENTS

The author would like to thank the following persons
and organisations for assistance with this booklet:
John and Jenny Aries, Cotleigh Brewery, Wiveliscombe:
Mick Aston: Bill Briggs: Mr D. Bromwich: Mrs C.E. Hancock
for access to and permission for use of family papers:
Mrs Pam Rolt: Mr D.N. Rapson, Ushers Brewery, Trowbridge:
Peter Seed, Head Brewer, Palmers Brewery, Bridport:
Somerset Records Office for permission to use Hancock
bottle labels, and Mr D.M.M. Shorrocks and the late
Mr Collis for ready advice: Mrs Shirley Vile for
typing the original manuscript: finally, my husband,
Iain, whose determination and energy have been fundamen-
tal in researching, recording and writing, and without
whom this booklet would never have been completed.

INTRODUCTION

In a county closely associated with cidermaking, it may seem surprising that at one time there were many brewers, both small and large, in full production. In 1859 the Harrison Harrod & Co.'s Post Office Directory listed ninety brewers in Somerset, approximately a third being small public house breweries. Over the years the number steadily declined until by 1939 only ten remained. This booklet deals with one of Somerset's major brewing organisations, Hancock's of Wiveliscombe.

Basically, beer is a fermented extract of malted barley, with hops added for flavour and preservation. Other additives such as sugar, rice, flaked maize and salts could be added at the brewer's desire. In the nineteenth century brewery the process was generally as follows. The malt was coarsely ground in the grist mill and mixed in the mash tun with hot water to produce the 'liquor'. This porridge stood for several hours to allow the sugars to dissolve into the liquid, now called 'wort', which was then run out through the false bottom of the mash tun, and the remaining grains sprayed or 'sparged' with more hot liquor. The wort then passed to the copper where it was boiled with hops. Afterwards it passed through a cooling process involving large open shallow vessels, sometimes with a 'fountain' spurting hot wort in the centre, and sometimes passing through a refrigerator, rather like a dairy cooler, as well. The cooled wort then ran into fermenting vessels where yeast was added to convert the sugar into alcohol and carbon dioxide. Fermentation lasted about five days, after which the beer was matured in conditioning tanks, then finings added to clear the beer. Finally the beer was racked into casks and 'dry hopped' — a handful of hops added to give extra aroma.

In the Victorian 'tower' brewery the process used gravity to great effect. The malt was stored in bins in the roof, cracked in the mill on the floor below, passed down to the mash tun below that, then the wort was dropped into the copper. It was then pumped back up to the top of the brewery for cooling in the airy room whose windows were fitted with open wooden louvres. After this the wort passed to the floor below for fermentation, then to the next floor down for maturation. Racking into casks took place on the ground floor, and casks ran down to the cellars below for storage.

The essentials to be considered when setting up a brewery were: a ready supply of good water; easy availability of malt or good barley, and hops; an efficient distribution system; and last, but not least, a thirsty market! Wiveliscombe was the ideal setting as far a William Hancock was concerned. The Porlock area provided good barley, sought after by brewers; and this was converted to malt at Hancock's own malthouse. Few brewers did not malt their own barley in the nineteenth century, the exceptions being smaller public houses; even farms often had their own malthouse. Hop growing in Somerset died out in the early part of the nineteenth century, and few tithe maps record 'hop yard'. Specialization of hop production had centred on Kent, Worcestershire and Hereford. As expertise in preserving the hop improved, so did transport, allowing wider use of those already favoured by London brewers.

The necessity for a pure and abundant water supply resulted in breweries being built as close to a good spring or well source as possible. In 1870 Frome brewers were accused of trying to solve their own water shortage at the town's expense, whilst Starkeys of Bridgwater were trying to prove that their supply was "perfectly free from any trace of sewage", presumably they had been accused of using the muddy Parrett waters!

Over the century the improvement in road and rail transport had an obvious effect. Hancock's was set up primarily for free trade, all of it local. As tied houses were purchased further and further away the horse-drawn dray-carts found it more difficult to cope, and rail links and the introduction of motor transport were eagerly seized on by brewers to supply their expanding markets. The drays started to disappear from the streets, and now only a few are still in use in the country as a whole, our nearest example being Wadsworths of Devizes. West Country brewers were pioneers of twentieth century steam road haulage and very many used steam waggons, mainly Fodens and later Sentinels.

Hancock's early market was the local farm labourers and woollen workers, on this trade was built the company which survived in some form for one hundred and fifty years.

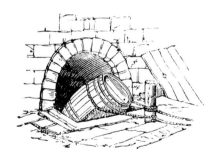

HISTORY

"The large brewery belonging to Mr. Hancock now represents the trade of the town. The upper waters of the Tone River (... fed by many pure springs in the parish of Wiveliscombe) are here converted into that sound and excellent beer which flows in a perennial stream to many distant towns - gladdening men's hearts and strengthening their bodies."

So wrote C. Waldron in 1883 in his account of Wiveliscombe. However, the brewery had small beginnings. The Hancock family were farmers at Ford, and William was the fourth son. His eldest brother, Philip, was a successful attorney, and his other two brothers emigrated to America. William began as a mercer in Wiveliscombe, later founding a bank there with his brother Philip. There were invasion scares as a result of Napoleon Bonaparte being declared Emperor, and the Hancocks rose to the call, Philip being a Lieutenant and William a Cornet of the Wiveliscombe troop of Yeomanry.

From letters still in the family's possession it would appear that William began his brewing business in 1806, perhaps at the top of High Street. His future wife, Mary Froude, writing to impress her uncle says "... Mr. Hancock, my dear uncle, is just the kind of man which suits me, a man of good sense without pride or affectation. He has been exceedingly fortunate in his business which consists of a Public Brewery and a Linen Drapers Shop, and himself and Brother carry on the Bank at Wiveliscombe. The shop he means at present, if all things go well, to give up in a few years". Philip mentions in the same year that the White Hart (formerly the Green Dragon) had been bought, and William sells "a great deal of beer" in it. At any rate, the business was successful enough for William to buy cottages and land on Golden Hill in 1807, demolish the buildings, and build a brewery and malthouse on the site. Wine cellars were built on the opposite side of the road in 1813, and the firm expanded as 'common brewers' selling their beer to the general public, not only through tied houses. The brewery was enlarged in 1830, with another storey being built over the brewhouse, and partly covering over the roadway between the brewhouse and malthouse. This expansion may have been as a result of the 1830 Beerhouse Act which removed the necessity for a prospective landlord to obtain a magistrate's licence, making it easier for householders to get a licence from the Excise Authority.

The 1842 tithe map shows William Hancock owning six public houses in the town, the Angel, Borough Inn, Half Moon Inn, Royal Oak Inn, White Hart Inn, and White Horse Inn. By his death in 1845 the tied house system had become well established, though he still owned less than twenty. His son, William Hancock the Younger, continued the expansion, and developed a beer stores at Cardiff which grew into a large brewery, quite separate from the Wiveliscombe one, but retaining close ties through the family links. By 1875 Hancock's had grown to be called "the largest brewery in the West of England", and in 1891 owned twenty-two houses, with the copyhold on one, and were lessees of a further thirty-eight. At this date William took three of his ten sons into partnership, and the firm became a private limited company in 1896. Expansion continued, with the tower built in 1897, and the brewery extended. The old malthouse was used for brewing, and the building on the west side of Golden Hill (later to be a cider factory) used for malting. An aerated water factory was built in 1900-1, and it was one of the first brewery companies to go into this type of production. Their ginger beer was considered so strong because of the addition of sugar that it competed with ordinary beer! At this stage the company employed upwards of one hundred people, and produced over 20,000 barrels of

beer per annum.   F. Willoughby Hancock rejoined the
firm after gaining experience in other breweries, a
common practice, in 1906 when the firm had eighty-five
licenced houses and assets of £67,000.   He was to
see this rise to well over £1,000,000 before his death
in 1959.

The cider factory was established on Golden
Hill in 1917, cider having previously been bought in
from local farmers.   Further public houses were acquired
when the firm bought the Old Brewery, Tiverton, from
the Devonport and Tiverton Brewery Co., Ltd in 1919.

By 1927 the firm had grown considerably from
its early small beginnings, and it amalgamated in that
year with S.W. Arnold & Sons Ltd of Rowbarton, Taunton.
In fact William Hancock & Sons (Wiveliscombe) Ltd continued to exist until 1934, with the issued share capital
being held by Arnold and Hancock or their nominees.
Stephen William Arnold founded his brewery in 1876
at Rowbarton on the site of a bone manure factory.
He came from a family of brewers at Wickwar in Glouces-
tershire, and survived on free trade, producing pale,
strong and mild ales, stouts and India Pale Ale.
His experience and enterprise led to a rapid expansion.
The West Somerset Brewery of Messrs Hatch was acquired
in 1897 for £27,000.   It was situated in St James
Street, Taunton, and the brewer's house still survives
as part of the Brewhouse Theatre to which it gives
its name.   Arnolds became a private limited company
in 1898, and in the following year acquired William
Hewett & Co. Ltd of Norton Fitzwarren for £52,000.
The firm developed trade with North Devon, and thus
the amalgamation of the two firms of Arnold and Hancock
became a sensible proposition for both companies.
Brewing continued at Rowbarton, but the emphasis was
very much on development at Wiveliscombe, which continued
malting for both breweries until 1938, when the Crewkerne
United Brewery was bought, and the malt produced at
the handsome Ashlands Brewery malthouse sent to
Rowbarton.

2: Brewery entrance from Golden Hill: cottages, l., offices, r. - 1974. (photo: Iain Miles)

3: Brewery yard with laboratory on upper floor on r. of arch - 1974. (photo: Iain Miles)

4: Lloyd Nurcome working the cask racking machine: circa 1955/59. (photo: Nick Thompson)

5: Rowbarton Brewery, Taunton: tower, centre background
  - 1974. (photo: Iain Miles)

6: Ashlands Maltings, Crewkerne - 1976. (photo: Derrick
  Warren)

By the 1950s there was a great move amongst breweries to amalgamate, and Arnold and Hancock sought a merger with another medium sized brewery. As a result, in 1955 Ushers Wiltshire Brewery Ltd, based at Trowbridge, acquired the whole of the issued share capital, with Arnold and Hancock Ltd continuing to operate as a wholly owned subsidiary. Ushers provided malt, and so malting ceased at Wiveliscombe and brewing at Rowbarton. Rationalization in 1959 turned Rowbarton into Ushers' regional office and depot, and brewing ceased at Wiveliscombe. Of the eighty people employed at the latter plant, only a percentage were re-employed at Rowbarton, being 'bused' out. In 1960 the plant and machinery at Wiveliscombe were sold or salvaged, and the premises disposed of. Within three years it became a chicken-processing plant for Ross Poultry Ltd. The following year Watney Mann Ltd acquired Ushers, and continued to use Rowbarton as a depot. Nine years later the cider factory at Golden Hill, scene of many local celebration dances, was burnt out and demolished.

It has been said that the choice in 1955 was between Ushers and Watneys, and that had the latter won control the brewery at Wiveliscombe would have remained open. Be that as it may, the depression resulting from the loss of such a major employer in the area left its mark, and caused much hardship and worry among the families who had been dependent on Hancock's for their livelihood.

AS EMPLOYERS

The company's relationship with its employees seems to have been fairly good, as with many family firms. There is no record of a strike, though the workers were not afraid to ask for a rise in wages. In 1899 the maltster applied for an increase of wages to make them equivalent to those paid to the brewers. The result is not recorded in the Minutes - it was left to the discretion of the Managing Directors, as was the question of unpunctuality in 1898. Hancock's appear to have been caring employers, arranging pensions, and giving bonuses for a job well done. "The sum of £5:5:0d to those of the Brewery Workmen who conduced to the satisfactory percentage of waste beer during the year", and on "satisfactory completion of the alterations to the Brewery Buildings and plant, bonuses of £50 to be given to Mr. F. Vickery, and £25 to Mr. Thos. Richards for their attention and services in superintending the work". This in addition to the bonuses paid at the presentation of accounts at ordinary general meetings. In 1922 these were, F.W. Hancock £100, F.W. Vickery £50, A.E. Collings £50, F. Greedy £40, W.F. Foster £40, Miss Balman £10, Miss Vallance £7:10:0, W. Giles £5, Jim Stone £3:10.0, and a bonus of 100% on the Directors' fees!

Unfortunately it is not possible to compare the wages of maltsters and brewers on an annual basis, as malting would only be done in a specific season, and not all the year round. Certainly the employees moved around, helping out with malting when necessary. The malting wages bill in 1906 was £435:10:9, whereas that for brewing was £1,644:7:5. Hancock's appear to have paid slightly higher than agricultural wages to the general staff as an incentive. The wages book for 1905 shows a total of sixty-one weekly paid wages, with the following breakdown:

FRIDAY 22 DECEMBER 1905

Department	Employees	Total	Individual wage range			
Brewing	23	£16:13:7	1s.3d.	to	£1:	0:0
Malting	21	£10: 7:3	9d.	"	£1:	0:9
A. Waters	3	£1:11:6	3s.9d.	"		16:6
Bottling	3	£1: 9:2	2s.6d.	"		16:0
General	24	£27:16:6	5s.5d.	"	£2:	2:6
Pensions	6	£1: 1:6	2s.0d.	"		5:0

Mechanics's wages, possibly included under "General",
amount to £13:15:2.   This makes a total payment for
the week of £58:19:6.   However, when salaried staff
are included the year's total looks likes this:

    Brewery and Malthouse employees £2,676
    Draymen £691
    Motor lorry drivers ....:.................. £208
    Clerical staff and Travellers £1,119

Young boys were employed on light duties at a low wage.
In 1908 5s.0d. was paid weekly to "Boy Babb"; by 1912
he was considered old enough to have his initial used
before his surname and be paid 14s.0d. weekly for bot-
tling.   Two boys were employed that year, "Boy Lewis"
and "Boy Webber".   It also appears that a few men
were employed on a casual basis.   It is interesting
to note that the Secretary to the Company was paid
£165 per annum in 1896, raised to £170 in 1897.
        As well as the mention of pensions paid in
1905 from the Wages Book, there are other references
to the Company's concern over this matter.   In 1897
pensions of £41:3:11 were paid, and later the firm
of Arnold and Hancock were to argue with the insurance
company that a proposed pension was not good enough
for one of their employees.
        In common with other forward-thinking firms
of the time, Hancock's organised events for their employees.   From 1900 onwards there are mentions of an
Annual Picnic.   In 1890 there is a reference in the

Brewing Journal "Began early for the men to go off to Cardiff races".

All in all, the brewery was run as a family concern, staff and employees were known to the Directors, many were called by their Christian or nicknames, and certain families had several of their members employed there. It appears that right up until the closure no employees were members of a union, and that "the Directors were always available for discussion". Certainly the Company seemed to have some concern for their employee's welfare. Apart from the pension scheme, houses were allowed to certain key workers. In 1898, "Mr. Harris' application for increase of salary refused on account of the short time he has been in the service of the Company. It was resolved that Mr. Harris be allowed a house free on his marriage". The Hancocks's attitude to the community doubtless helped to foster 'family feeling'.

IN THE COMMUNITY

        The Hancocks were an important local family,
with a large farm, having already founded a bank in
1803.   They involved themselves very much in local
affairs;   for instance, in 1923 the Wellington and
Wiveliscombe Directory notes the following:

    Mr F.W. Hancock — local representative of the
                         Wellington Board of Guard-
                         ians, on the Urban District
                         Council, Council School Lo-
                         cal Managers Board, Overseer
                         of the Poor, Trustee of the
                         United Services Fund Welfare
                         Committee.
    Mrs F.W. Hancock — President of Wiveliscombe
                         Girls Club
    Mr F.E. Hancock — Lay representative on the
                         Parish Church Council, Pre-
                         sident of the Football
                         (Rugby) Club.
    Mrs F,E. Hancock — President of the Horticul-
                         tural Society.
    Mr P.F. Hancock — Vice-Chairman of the Urban
                         District Council, Sidesman
                         at St Andrews Church, and
                         Chairman of Wiveliscombe
                         Gymkhana Commmttee.
    Mrs P.F. Hancock — President of the Wiveliscombe
                         Tennis Club and Chairman of
                         the Recreation Ground
                         Committee.

How did they have time for brewing?

All the sons of William Hancock the Younger
were rugby players, seven of them playing for Somerset.
Two of them, P.F. Hancock and F.E. (Frank) Hancock,
gained international honours, the former captaining
England and the latter Wales. Hence the comment in
the Brewing Journal when disaster faced one brew, "I
am in a fainting condition. I wont risk it again,
not even for England v Wales at Cardiff Ground!"
Frank Hancock introduced the modern line-up of four
three-quarters in 1885 whilst captain of the Cardiff
club. The Hancocks were also prominent in local festi-
vities. Their malting floor, and later the cider
factory floors, were used for special events, Coronation
celebrations, Jubilees, etcetera.

The siren on the Brewery tower which marked
the starting and ending of work periods for staff was
also used as a fire alarm to alert the local volunteer
brigade, and during the Second World War the Brewery
manned an Auxilliary Fire Service tender pump. An
amusing anecdote of the same period was told by a local
resident. The Ministry of Food asked a butcher to
ensure that a week's supply of meat be kept frozen
locally. He got Mr Willoughby Hancock to allow the
use of a refrigerator in one of the cellars. Weeks
later the butcher was told that there was a horrible
smell of "off meat". It seems that every time beer
was sent down to the refrigerator (cold store) the
rise in temperature had thawed the meat, and later
it froze again!

AS BREWERS

Hancock's appear to have been traditional brewers, using accepted methods of the day.   The Brewery had its own water pipeline, reservoir and ancillary apparatus connected to a water supply fed by springs at Coate Farm (owned by the Hancock family).   Water found in nature is never chemically pure.   The presence of calcium sulphate in the water helps in two ways; it gives clarity in the finished product by preventing a starch haze forming, and it inhibits the extraction of undesirable resins from the hops.   The waters at Burton-on-Trent had this quality, meaning that brewers there could use plenty of hops, giving their beer a full flavour and good keeping qualities, thus making Burton Bitters famous throughout England.   However, waters containing little or no calcium sulphate are more suitable for brewing mild ales and stouts, or can be treated with salts for bitter brewing (Burtonising).   Hancock's used Burton Crystals (between 1890 and 1897 bought from Roberts & Co.), Boakes Salts and "pure salt".   The Brewing Journal of 1889/90 notes on May 25 1889 when brewing a bitter ale "Omitted to put Boakes preparations in sparge liquor.   Used $2\frac{1}{2}$ lbs salt".

The malt used was practically all English. The Brewing Journal of 1894-5 shows that they used 3,428 qtrs of malt in that year.   Undoubtedly much of this was malted in their own malthouse,   though the Purchase Ledger of 1889-97 shows Hancock's were buying a little malt from Dublin, which was not an uncommon practice in the brewing industry at that date, but entries in the Brewing Journal show that "foreign" malt seems to have been regarded with some suspicion by the Head Brewer.   "New Bute Dock malt made from Welsh Barley - about average lot", and about Californian malt "It had a few mouldy ones which we would

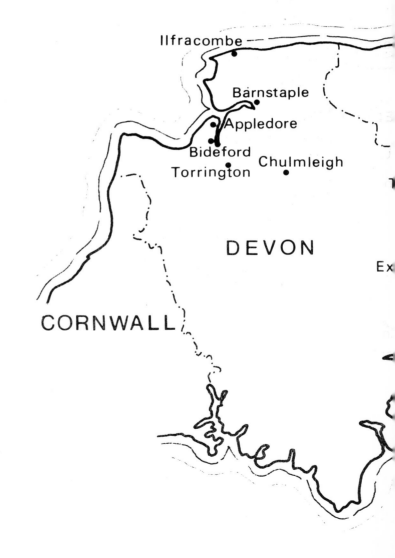

Ilfracombe

Barnstaple

Appledore

Bideford
Torrington

Chulmleigh

DEVON

Ex

CORNWALL

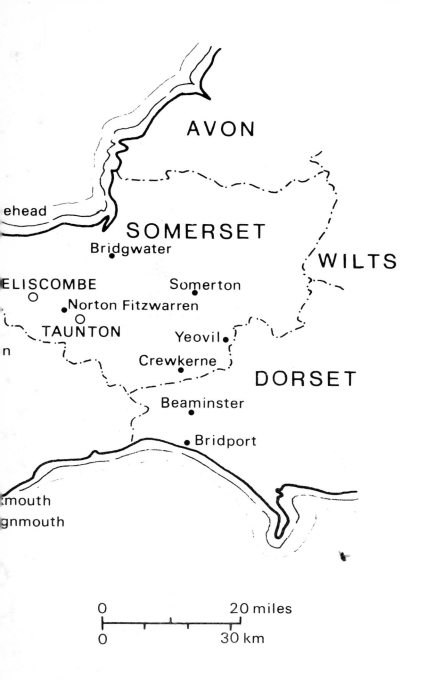

AVON

ehead

SOMERSET

Bridgwater

WILTS

ELISCOMBE
○

Somerton

Norton Fitzwarren
○

TAUNTON

Yeovil

n

Crewkerne

DORSET

Beaminster

Bridport

mouth
gnmouth

| 0 | | | | 20 miles |
| 0 | | | | 30 km |

Map: David Greenfield

17

rather have avoided if possible", or "The Chilean malt
from Newport was almost dangerously slack" and "This
finished the Danubian malt for which we must be thankful.
Quite three-quarters of it was ungerminated and in
reality steely barley. It took me so long to brew
that some of it was dried three times.".

The majority of barley for malting came from
local farmers, the furthest recorded distance being
Bristol, though it is posible that this barley, being
bought from dealers, may well have come from much further
afield. Local barley grown around the coastal areas
of West Somerset was much prized all over the county,
and possibly outside as well. Hancock's also sold
their excess malt from the malthouse, much of it to
the Cardiff firm of William Hancock & Co.

In April 1889 they experimented with an all
malt Stock Bitter Ale (SBA) to see how it would keep
in comparison with part sugar brews. This must have
been successful for by 1894 it had become standard
practice for their SBA. In 1888 they experimented
with maltose provided by a Dutchman and a German.
"They neither of them knew anything about brewing or
anything else. Davis put them all off the scent by
giving them the Excise SG thousands and all. I expect
we shall be worried to death owing to this step.
They made us a present of the maltose and well they
might as we had a deadly horror that it was made from
diseased potatoes. They tried hard to impress on
us that the maltose gives more extract than Gortais
but we told them the proof of the pudding was in the
eating! The Extract fell just short of their expecta-
tions though we had a fair crop of yeast. However,
the beer it tastes thin and nasty and not as good as
ordinary 14 UGA. We are to send a sample $4\frac{1}{2}$ gallons
to our teachers. They can supply us @ 11/- per cwt.
They asked £500,000 for their patent. Davis and I
decided to consider a few years before we offer them
two pence."

However, despite their concern over malt, when

the Head Brewer of a present day firm was shown a few
pages from the 1889-90 Brewing Journal his comment
was: "... their Extracts were very low, using poor
malt", though it must be remembered that improvements
in the brewing process were continuing to be made,
and also deficiencies in the malt might be made up
by the addition of sugar. The son of a fairly large
firm of Somerset brewers (now defunct) thought that
the malt used in this present day by the brewing industry
"... my father would have thrown out of the window!"
        Much of the hops used was bought from London
dealers, though some were bought direct from Worcestershire and Kent. In early days only English hops were
used by Hancock's, but by 1912 Californian hops were
used as well. In 1894 31,995 lbs of hops were used,
with an allowance of 50 lbs per week in addition for
dry hopping. Hancock's tended to keep in a fair stock
of hops, and in September 1902 the Directors's Minute
Book records that over a year's supply of hops was
in stock. The Head Brewer's favourites appear to
have been Crumps and Kempsons Worcesters. "Crumps
and Kempson hops were chosen from the best pockets
and beat the other hops in looks at any rate. Taps
slightly green but of a glorious flavour." Some Sussex
hops were tried. "Note Sussex hops, we thought them
milder than usual for Stock (SBA) so used 20 lb. extra."
Caves hops came in for quite a bit of criticism.

"Had to scrape Caves Hops a good deal as there was
a thick crust over the whole pocket." "We opened
rather a soft and bad pocket of Caves hops." "Caves
hops finished, by cutting off the crust carefully.
We have brewed with them most successfully. Quite
20 lbs per pocket thrown away." However, Chapman's
were approved of. "Chapman's '87 are very good hops.
We have sent four pockets of them to Newport. More
fools we."
        In 1890 yeast was bought from Watsons & Co.
of London, and the Brewing Journal records "Yeast from

Newport, it looks very good.   C D says it cannot be
otherwise.", but as no other purchases of yeast are
recorded, it is most likely that a culture of yeast
was kept going for their own use.   Flaked maize was
being used in 1902, and sugar was added sometime after
1847.   In the year 1894-5 542 lbs were used, and the
experiment with SBA from malt only has already been
mentioned.   From 1889 some of the saccharum was bought
from Garton Hill & Co., famous sugar refiners, who
at that time owned the Anglo-Bavarian Brewery at Shepton
Mallet.   In 1890 finings and isinglass were being
bought from Stratford-upon-Avon and London.

From the Brewing Journal of 1889-90 it appears
that Hancock's were brewing six days a week, not Sundays,
with a total of 288 brews a year.   A comparison of
the two brewing years 1888-9 and 1889-90 is as follows:

	Total Barrels	BA	BB	XX	P(Porter, Stout)	GA
1888-89	22,347	839	915	16,591	1,538	2,463
1889-90	24,070	953	857	17,162	2,481	1,517
Increase	1,723	114		571	1,043	53
Decrease			58			

The titles BA (Best or Bitter Ale), BB (Best Bitter),
XX and GA, were used to differentiate between the beers
produced by a single brewery, some using special names
such as Antler Ale.

It is the practice in modern breweries to brew
a particular type of beer regularly on the same day
each week, but Hancock's at this date appear to have
been brewing according to demand.   The number of barrels
produced in one day varies from 44 (SBA) to 106 (GA).
To give an idea of the quantity of materials used,
in the year 1894-5 3,428 qtrs malt, 542 lbs sugar,
31,995 lbs hops (plus approximately 2,402 lbs for dry
hopping) produced 16,087 barrels.

From the few details of the plant at the brewery
at the time, it would seem that Hancock's kept up with

the general trends in brewing, being neither great
innovators, nor lagging behind, but rather waiting
a period to see how new ideas worked out.   Although
Taylor's patent (No. 4032) laid down the basis for
the method of heating modern coppers in 1816, low pressure steam boiling did not apparently make much progress
in Britain until after 1900, possibly because of the
availability of cheap coal.   Certainly Hancock's
were well situated for coal from Wales or the North
Somerset coalfield.   In 1890 there are references
to a dome for one of the coppers, which was lifted
up and down, and the Brewing Journal for 1897 refers
to both an "open copper" and a "pressure copper", with
the first cryptic mention of "Boiled under pressure"
on 25 August 1887.   In 1894 they were using up to
five fermenting vessels, though the type and size are
not clear.   The Brewing Journal of 1898 records "Last
time the Old Fridge was used 20. 1. 98.", and the new
one was most likely of the Baudelot type   -   similar
to a dairy cooler.   Copper coolers, supplied by Adlams
of Bristol, as was much of the plant, were in use in
1903 when five defective plates were discovered in
one.   Adlams denied any liability, but only charged
£10 towards the cost of renewal.   This was possibly
the "new cooler" mentioned in 1897.

The problem of gauging the exact amount of
beer in a cask was a perennial worry for all brewers.
In 1903 Hancock's tested and approved one form of indicator, which seems to have been a great success as four
months later they ordered a similar indicator for jars
and siphons.   In the same year a cask washer capable
of washing four casks at a time was purchased, at a
total cost of £102.

In 1902 the old stationary engine and boiler

were sold to Adlams for £100, and a new gas engine
installed (using no doubt Town Gas – see later gas
producer plant installed in 1905) at an estimated saving
of 4s. per day.   At the same date the purchase of
a grain dryer was confirmed.   The cost, £420, seems
rather high.   It would have been used to dry the spent
grain from the mash tun before being collected by local
farmers, or being fed to the Brewery horses as Hancock's
were doing.   They estimated that each horse consumed
28 lbs per week, making a cost of 1s. per horse per
week.   A Lancashire boiler of 1896, by Adlams, with
a maximum working pressure of 60 lbs per sq. in. was
discontinued on 11 January 1926, and a John Thompson
installed (1925) with a maximum pressure of 100 lbs
per sq. in.   Later another boiler joined this one,
and the two lasted until the Brewery closed.   It has
been said that they were the first to be converted
locally to oil.

AS BUSINESSMEN

William Hancock the Elder was an astute business-
man.   He was already a banker and farmer before starting
the Wiveliscombe Brewery, and undoubtedly used his
commercial knowledge to great effect in the venture.
His son, William Hancock the Younger, continued in
this good business sense, and under the partnership
of him and three of his sons the Brewery grew and flour-
ished.   There were constant improvements to the buildings: in 1897 the new Tower block was built, telephones
were installed in 1907, and radiators were put in the
office in 1913.   Indeed the Directors seemed to consider
any expense for their comfort (2 September 1902, an
outlay of £40 sanctioned for office alterations: 14
November 1902, £25 extra: 23 April 1903 "Office alterations ... had cost £122" - with no further comment!),
whilst arguing with Worthingtons over an extra $2\frac{1}{2}$%
discount on an account of £500 per annum.   However,
the gas producer plant, a Crossley No. 3, installed
in October 1905, proved a sound investment.   By the
third week of working it cost 1/10d. per day, whereas
Town Gas had cost 8/6d. per day!
       Breweries were notorius for fires, and Hancock's
had their share of small fires, though nothing serious.
A note of reduction in the fire insurance premium of
1896 shows that the Brewery buildings were insured
for £8,475.   In 1908 the idea of Brewery Fire Brigade
was considered, and taken up.   A small hand-drawn
fire cart and fire buckets were purchased for £50,
and the Brewery hooter was installed.   The latter
was used as a general fire siren for many years.   However, insurance of licences was considered "not necessary
for the business of this company".
       Hancock's took a lively interest in local af-
fairs, subscriptions were paid to local charities such
as the Wiveliscombe Nursing Association, and shares

were bought in the Wiveliscombe Quarry Company, and Minehead Pier Company (Hancock's subscribed £3,000 to the latter). The Purchase Ledger of 1889-97 shows Hancock's experimenting, trying out bottles from the South Wales Glass Manufacturing Company, Powell & Rickets of Bristol, and Prices of Bristol. It also shows the wide area from which supplies were drawn, with finings from Stratford-upon-Avon and London, yeast from London, barrels from Bedminster and Taunton, corks, shives and spiles from Bristol, labels from Deptford, hoops from Staffordshire, iron bushels from Sheffield, and kiln tiles from Walsingham.

However, as businessmen they were not without fault. In the final accounts of 1925 it was discovered that the Company was making a book loss of 0.2d. per dozen bottles from the Aerated Water Department, though gross profit of £836:13:2 was made on Aerated Waters alone that year.

7: Prince and relief carter, Frank Stone, at Golden Hill
exit: barrel-shaped horse brass. (photo: Nick Thompson)

8: Hancock's first Foden at Foden's Elworth Works: Edwin Foden in background (photo: courtesy Bill Briggs)

9: Hancock's Commer 58: driver Roy Conibere, mate Tommy Harris, circa 1955/59. (photo: Nick Thompson)

TRANSPORT

Always looking at the latest innovations, the
Company started to consider the purchase of a steam
waggon in September 1902. The Directors's Minute
Book entry for March 1904 remarks that a Foden would
cost £620, with a 10% discount for cash in one month.
In June of the same year the Minute Book notes that
the steam waggon had "now been working 5 weeks. A
competent driver has been engaged at 25/- a week –
at present the waggon takes 3 men to work it but it
is hoped to reduce it in the winter to 2 men and 1
lad.". It was a 5 tonner, with outside plate frames,
registrastion number Y200. In Foden's 1926 catalogue
a testimonial is printed from Willoughby Hancock regar-
ding this vehicle, in which he estimates that she had
travelled well over 100,000 miles and been subject
to harder gradients and surfaces in West Somerset and
North Devon than a London vehicle would have been.
"... it is no exaggeration to say that the engine
pulls as well today as she did on the first day she
went out of the yard." This was written in 1921,
ironically by 1923 she had been sold.

Her success led to the purchase in 1908 of
a second Foden, a 3 tonner, M1940. The new vehicle
cost £550, had two speeds, 12 and 5 miles per hour,
whilst her back wheels were fitted with twin solid
rubber tyres and her front with single ones. Later
a petrol Lacre motor lorry and an Albion car were bought.
However, the third party insurance was increased following various accidents: first a mare was killed by
one of the Fodens, then a carter, a cyclist and a pedes-
trian were hurt in three separate incidents. Eventually
the accident-prone Lacre driver was sacked.

By 1925 the Company owned eight motor vehicles;
the steam waggon, a Daimler, an Alldays and 5 Peerless.
Two further Fodens were purchased later, a second-

hand 5 tonner, MA862, and a 6 tonner C type, YB9635, which finally went for scrap in 1948 after being rebuilt as a tar sprayer by one of its owners.

A list of journeys for 10 January 1933 gives the following:

"Waterrow, Bampton, Dulverton	Foden	35	(presumably
Barnstable	Peerless 1	55	miles)
Minehead, Porlock	Peerless 5	20	" "
Withypool	Dodge	6	" "
Town (this being a dray)	J. Hodge	7	" "
Barnstable3, West Anstey 2	Rail		"

In 1938 nine lorrymen are named: F.B. Vickery, J. Salter, E. Mullins, W. Conibere, J. and W. Dulborough, E. Salter, E. Humries and Gilbert Smith, whilst the workshop was run by three men.

However, horse-drawn dray-carts were used for local deliveries until 1958, the last horse being 'Prince'. In June of that year the monthly executive's conference notes that he was then very old and "actually doing more work than ever". The Chairman, F.W., Hancock, stated that he would not be replaced or "sent to the knackers". By December he had been destroyed because of failing health and age, and local deliveries were being made by light lorry.

STRUCTURES IN 1985

After closure the Rowbarton site, preserved for some years as Watney's store, was finally demolished for housing in 1982. The Ashlands Malting at Crewkerne still stands, as does the malthouse at Norton Fitzwarren, though the brewery has gone. The only remains of the West Somerset Brewery in St James Street, Taunton, is now the Georgian brewer's house, the other buildings lying under the Brewhouse Theatre and car park.

For many years the Wiveliscombe Brewery was a chicken-processing factory, only part of the buildings being used, the rest left as an empty shell. Today, while the walls remain, the interior has undergone a change. The roof of the original malthouse has been renewed and the top floor containing the storage bins removed. The floors below, though empty, remain intact. The slate water-storage cistern sited at first floor level between the brewery and malthouse has gone. Possibly this was made from slate from the local Treborough Quarry. In the brewery the lowest level of cellars has been filled in, and many of the fixtures, even some floors, removed. Parts, including the boiler-house, have been turned into small factory units, two being leased by 'real ale' breweries, the Golden Hill Brewery and the Cotleigh Brewery, which grew out of the CAMRA campaign. Perhaps William Hancock would have been amused at this strange irony!

GLOSSARY

Aerated water – carbonated drink, modern equivalent called soft drinks, such as lemonade.

Barrel – cask holding 36 gallons.

Bitter – well-hopped light coloured beer.

Brewing Journal – Brewer's 'diary' recording full details of each brew.

Common brewer – brewer selling his beer to the public, not necessarily through tied houses.

Cooler – large open vessel into which hot wort is run to cool to correct temperature for yeast to act for fermentation.

Copper – vessel in which wort is boiled with hops before being fermented.

Dray – Horse-drawn waggon used to carry casks and bottles from brewery to public house.

Excise – Customs and Excise. The duty charged on quantity and strength of beer, the strength determined by taking the specific gravity (SG).

Fermentation – process for converting wort into beer by use of yeast.

Finings – addition of isinglass to clarify beer. (In the past other items such as eggshells, chalk and sugar, treacle and oyster shells were used).

Free trade – public houses not tied to one brewery, so able to pick and choose the beers they sell

Hogshead – cask of 54 gallons capacity.

India Pale Ale – beer of quality and clarity originally brewed to withstand transportation to India.

Isinglass – obtained from swim bladder of the sturgeon, used to clear of 'fine' beer.

Malt – barley grains allowed to germinate and then arrested by heat in a kiln – a rich source of natural sugars.

Malthouse – building used to convert barley to malt.

28

Maltose   -   a malt extract.
Pocket   -   name for a sack containing hops.
Porter   -   a mixture of old, bitter and mild ales, said to
             have been popular with London porters,   hence
             the name. Brewed best with soft water.
Racking   -   filling casks with beer.
Refrigerator   -   apparatus of metal   tubes   through   which
                   icy cold water is pumped whilst   the   hot
                   wort is run over the outside (or vice ve-
                   rsa), to cool it quickly   so   that   yeast
                   can be added.
Saccharum   -   sugar.
Shive   -   wooden bung for cask, having a central core that
            can be knocked in for a spile to be inserted.
Slack   -   malt containing too high a proportion of moist-
            ure (not made or stored well).
Specific gravity   -   SG: measured by comparing given wei-
                       ght of a liquid with that of pure wa-
                       ter.   Use of sugar will increase SG
                       proportionally, as home brewers and
                       wine makers will know. For instance,
                       pure water has an SG of 1,000:   5%
                       cane sugar solution has 1,020 SG, 10%
                       cane sugar solution has 1,040 SG.
Spile   -   soft wooden peg knocked into centre of shive to
            allow carbon dioxide to escape.
Steely   -   hard, therefore difficult to extract sugar.
Wort   -   unfermented beer.
Yeast   -   microscopic fungus used to ferment wort in beer.

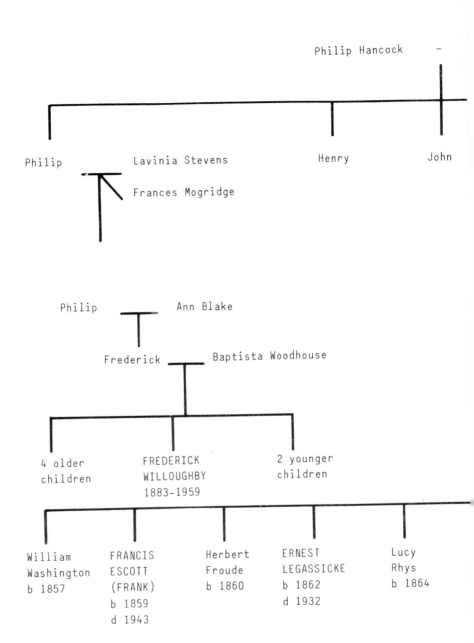

Philip Hancock   –

Philip   Lavinia Stevens   Henry   John

Frances Mogridge

Philip   Ann Blake

Frederick   Baptista Woodhouse

4 older
children

FREDERICK
WILLOUGHBY
1883–1959

2 younger
children

William
Washington
b 1857

FRANCIS
ESCOTT
(FRANK)
b 1859
d 1943

Herbert
Froude
b 1860

ERNEST
LEGASSICKE
b 1862
d 1932

Lucy
Rhys
b 1864

Mary Crocker

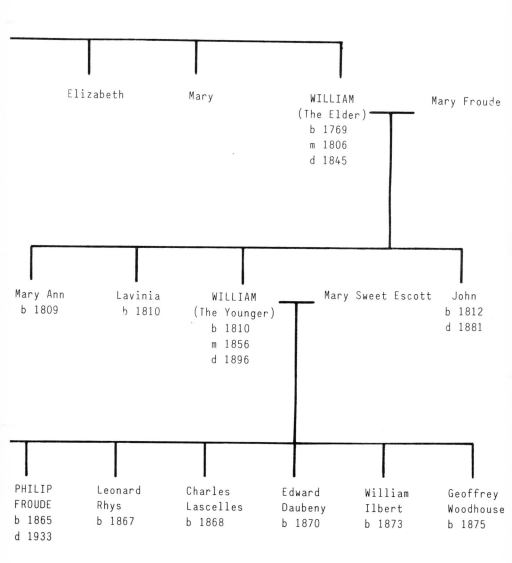

Elizabeth

Mary

WILLIAM
(The Elder)
b 1769
m 1806
d 1845

Mary Froude

Mary Ann
b 1809

Lavinia
b 1810

WILLIAM
(The Younger)
b 1810
m 1856
d 1896

Mary Sweet Escott

John
b 1812
d 1881

PHILIP
FROUDE
b 1865
d 1933

Leonard
Rhys
b 1867

Charles
Lascelles
b 1868

Edward
Daubeny
b 1870

William
Ilbert
b 1873

Geoffrey
Woodhouse
b 1875

REFERENCES

Somerset County Records Office   - Hancock   depositions,
                                      DD/HCK boxes 1-29
                                  - Tithe Map of Wivelis-
                                      combe, 1842
Private letters of the Hancock family
C. Waldron <u>Some Account of Wiveliscombe</u>, 1883
<u>North Devon Journal</u>, 1918
<u>Somerset</u>, 1875, County Topographies, edited by Kellys
Local Trade Directories, 1822-1939

The author would be interested to receive any informa-
tion on other Somerset breweries and can be contacted
at: Rose Cottage, Lower Durston, Taunton, Somerset,
TA3 5AH.